Zaner-Bloser

HANDWRITING

BASIC SKILLS and APPLICATION

WALTER B. BARBE, *Ph.D.*

Editor-in-Chief, *Highlights for Children*;
Adjunct Professor, The Ohio State University

VIRGINIA H. LUCAS, *Ph.D.*

Professor of Education
Wittenberg University, Springfield, Ohio

THOMAS M. WASYLYK

Master Penman and Handwriting Specialist;
Past President, International Association of Master Penmen,
Engrossers, and Teachers of Handwriting

CLINTON S. HACKNEY

Master Penman and Professional Handwriting Consultant,
Tampa, Florida

LOIS A. BRAUN

Supervisor, Elementary Curriculum,
Santa Monica-Malibu (California) Unified School District

The Nathan Hale Schoolhouse at East Haddam, Connecticut. Nathan Hale, scholar, patriot, soldier, taught here in 1773-1774. He died in the service of his country in 1776. His last words were, "I only regret that I have but one life to lose for my country."

Zaner-Bloser, Inc., Columbus, Ohio

Many years ago students wrote on small slate boards with chalk or on parchment with quill pens.

Youth is the time for study

Write the sentence.

_____
_____
_____
_____
_____
_____
_____
_____
_____
_____

CHECK-UP

	CORRECT	INCORRECT		CORRECT	INCORRECT
letter formation	☐	☐	slant (cursive)	☐	☐
alignment and proportion	☐	☐	spacing	☐	☐
vertical quality (manuscript)	☐	☐	line quality	☐	☐

3

Manuscript and Cursive Lower-case Letters

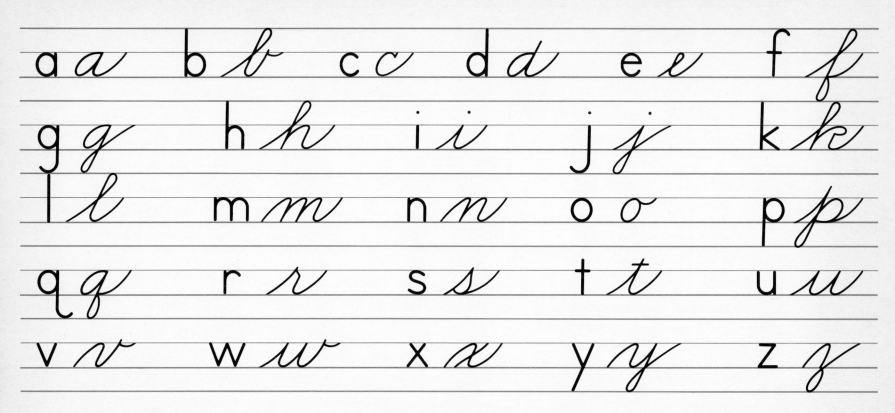

aa bb cc dd ee ff
gg hh ii jj kk
ll mm nn oo pp
qq rr ss tt uu
vv ww xx yy zz

Look at the words. How are they different?

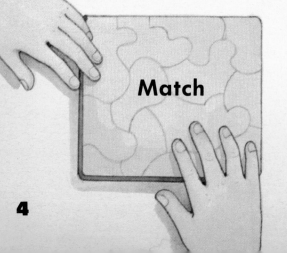

Match

bicycle *bicycle*

a   e
h   a
e   s
s   h

d   w
m   p
w   m
p   d

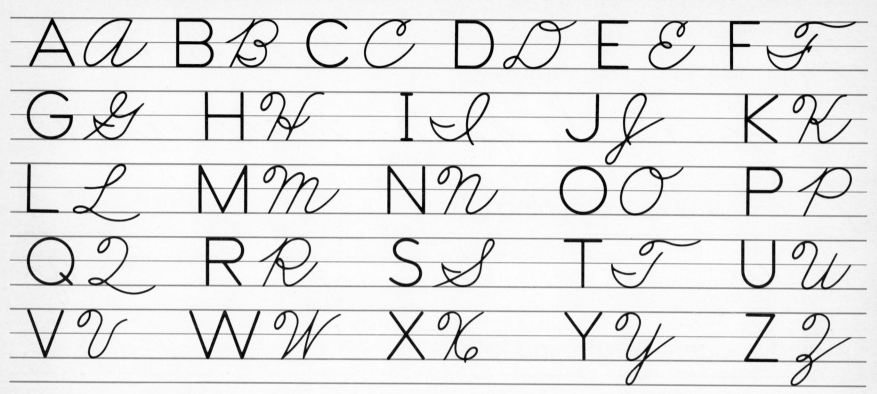

A A B B C C D D E E F F
G G H H I I J J K K
L L M M N N O O P P
Q Q R R S S T T U U
V V W W X X Y Y Z Z

Match

C   K
K   T
V   V
T   C

Y   I
M   O
I   Y
O   M

Grouping Cursive Letters

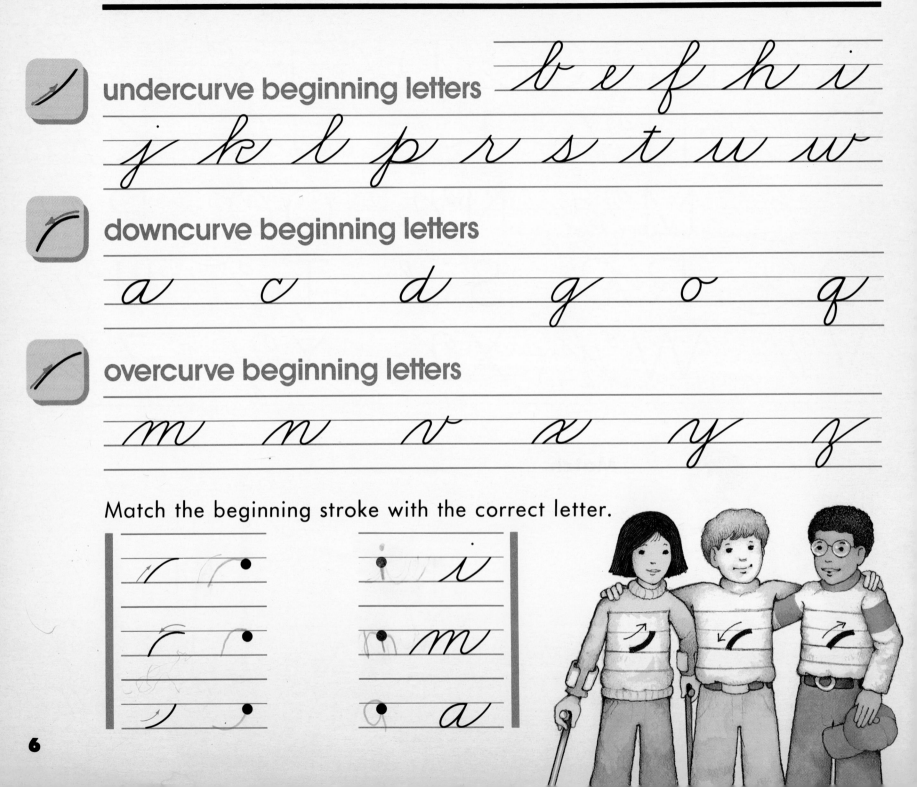

undercurve beginning letters

b e f h i
j k l p r s t u w

downcurve beginning letters

a c d g o q

overcurve beginning letters

m n v x y z

Match the beginning stroke with the correct letter.

i

m

a

6

Paper Position

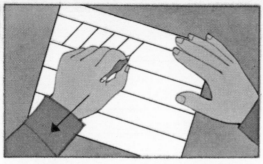

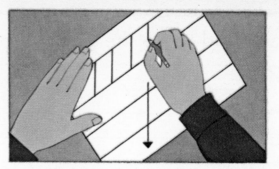

pull toward left elbow   pull toward midsection

Slant

Is your paper or book positioned correctly? Trace and write the slant strokes. Pull your strokes in the proper direction. Remember to shift your paper or book.

////////////   **(shift paper)** //////

Add the slant strokes to complete the letters.

l l b b P P m m

w w k k m m y y

Is your paper or book positioned correctly? Trace and write the slant strokes.

///////////   //////////

Backward Oval

The backward oval contains two of the motions used to make cursive letters.

Trace and write the backward oval.

Do your backward ovals slant?   ☑ **YES**   ☐ **NO**

Undercurve

The undercurve is part of the backward oval.

Trace and write the short undercurve.

Trace and write the tall undercurve.

My undercurves are: **CORRECT** ☐   **INCORRECT** ☐

The undercurve is used to begin fourteen lower-case letters. Find them on page 4.

Trace and write the undercurve-slant motion.

Undercurve Letters

Trace and write the strokes and letters.

Trace and write the joinings.

Undercurve Letters

Trace and write the letters, joinings, and word.

u $\mathcal{u}$ $\mathcal{u}$ $\mathcal{u}$ _____ _____ _____ $\mathcal{u}$

$\mathcal{u}$ _____ _____ _____ $\mathcal{u}$

$\mathcal{tu}$ $\mathcal{tu}$ _____ _____ $\mathcal{tu}$

W $\mathcal{w}$ $\mathcal{w}$ $\mathcal{w}$ _____ _____ $\mathcal{w}$

$\mathcal{w}$ _____ _____ $\mathcal{w}$

$\mathcal{wi}$ $\mathcal{wi}$ _____ _____ $\mathcal{wi}$

$\mathcal{wit}$ _____ _____ _____

Pencil Position

left-handed

right-handed

Where do animals live?

u w

Trace the **w** or **u** in each word.
Match each animal to where it lives.

whale •   • *underground*

worm •   *woods*

wolf •   • *underwater*

Draw lines through the slant strokes in these words.
How many slant strokes are there?

whale ☐   *tube* ☐

web ☐   *walrus* ☐

How many undercurves are in these words?

flew ☐   *shut* ☐   *rub* ☐

Undercurve Letters

Trace and write the strokes and letters.

e e

l l

Write the words.

we

let

$tile$

Write the two letters together.

t + i = ti

l + t =

w + e =

i + e =

l + l =

i + l =

w + i =

e + l =

1. tie

2. well

3. wilt

4. tell

Look at each word and picture. Write the words.

1. _____

2. _____

3. _____

4. _____

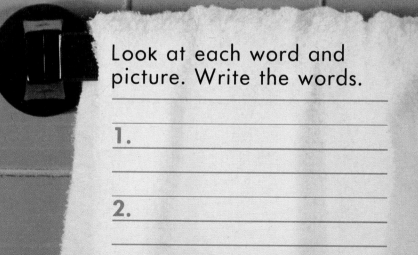

13

Undercurve Letters

Trace and write the strokes and letter.

_f_

feel

life

Write the words.

Line Quality

save
CORRECT

circus
too light

thirteen
wavering

vacant
too heavy

14

Manuscript Maintenance

Find a word in the puzzle to match each clue.
Look across or down each row.
Write the words in manuscript.

a little insect

_____

_____

a rock

_____

_____

a story

_____

_____

begin

_____

_____

ten minus nine

_____

_____

opposite of right

_____

_____

s c e l

s t o n e

d a n t f

g r e f t

h t a l e

Undercurve Letters

Trace and write the strokes and letters.

b b b _____ b

b b _____ b

b _____ b

be be _____ be

bl bl _____ bl

Alignment

CORRECT

little

INCORRECT

little

Write the words.

little _____

bull _____

Alignment—the evenness of the letters along the baseline and along their tops. Letters of the same size should be of the same height.

My alignment is correct.   YES ☐   NO ☐

16

Jean planned to show her young bull at the county fair. She wanted to give him a bath. Jean got the soap and filled a tub with water.
Look what happened.

Write these words.

bull _____

tub _____

wet _____

Use the words above to finish the sentences.

The _____ *fell*.

Jean got _____.

The _____ *is dry*.

17

Undercurve Letters

Trace and write the strokes and letters. Write the joinings and words.

r r r

r r

r r r

ru   ruler

wr   write

s s s

s s s

Write the words.

sew   rust

stir   flies

18

Find three words to write under each heading.

fur less rust butter sweet us rest still rise street bus letter

Words that end with the letter **s**.

bus

Words that end with the letter **r**.

Words that begin with the letter **s**.

Words that begin with the letter **r**.

Write these letter combinations in cursive.

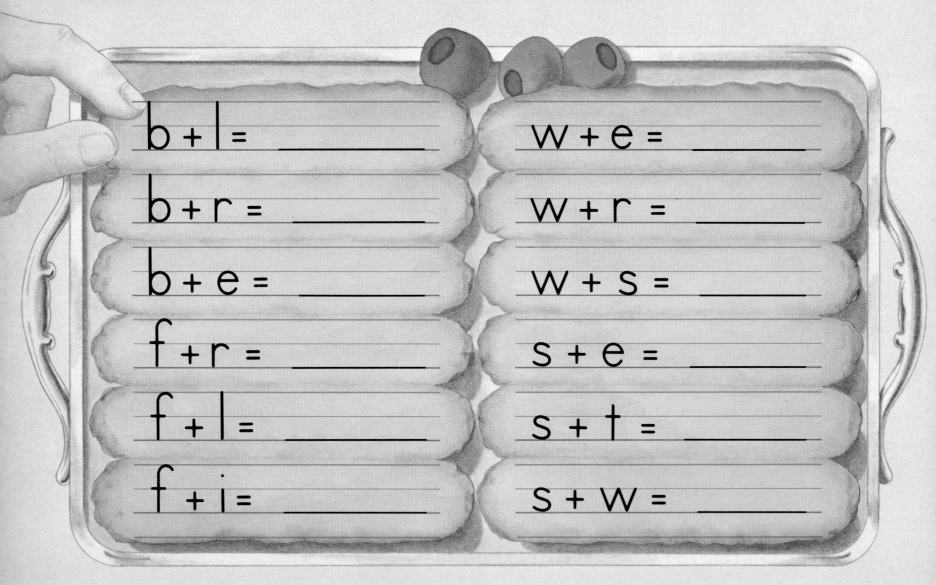

b + l = _____   w + e = _____

b + r = _____   w + r = _____

b + e = _____   w + s = _____

f + r = _____   s + e = _____

f + l = _____   s + t = _____

f + i = _____   s + w = _____

Which of the following letters extend slightly above the midline?
Write them.

_____ *e r s w w* _____

20

How many words can you make
using these letters?

b e i r u w t s l f

Write your words.

1. _____   6. _____

2. _____   7. _____

3. _____   8. _____

4. _____   9. _____

5. _____   10. _____

Undercurve Letters

Trace and write the strokes and letters. Write the words.

h

l l l _____ _____ *l*

h h h _____ _____ *h*

h h h _____ _____ *h*

h h _____ _____ *h*

hill _____ *hut*

k

l l l _____ _____ *l*

k k k _____ _____ *k*

k k k _____ _____ *k*

kit _____ *risk*

Write the words. Complete the sentence.

week

kettle

fire

hurt

risk

her

his

hike

The kettle is full.

T

Undercurve Letters

Trace and write the strokes and letters. Write the words.

j j

j j

j j

jet   jewel

p p

p p

p p

p p

push   pull

pepper

Everyone has a job to help keep our school clean. Write the words.

help

keep

just

put

Trace the letter **j**.

job 1

Pick up litter.

job 2

Clean up after lunch.

job 3

Keep your desk neat.

Complete the sentence.

Pick up litter.

Pick

j p

25

Fourteen lower-case letters begin with an undercurve. Write them.

Look at the manuscript words. Write them in cursive.

brush _____

wrist _____

three _____

wet _____

purple _____

bubbles _____

Manuscript Maintenance

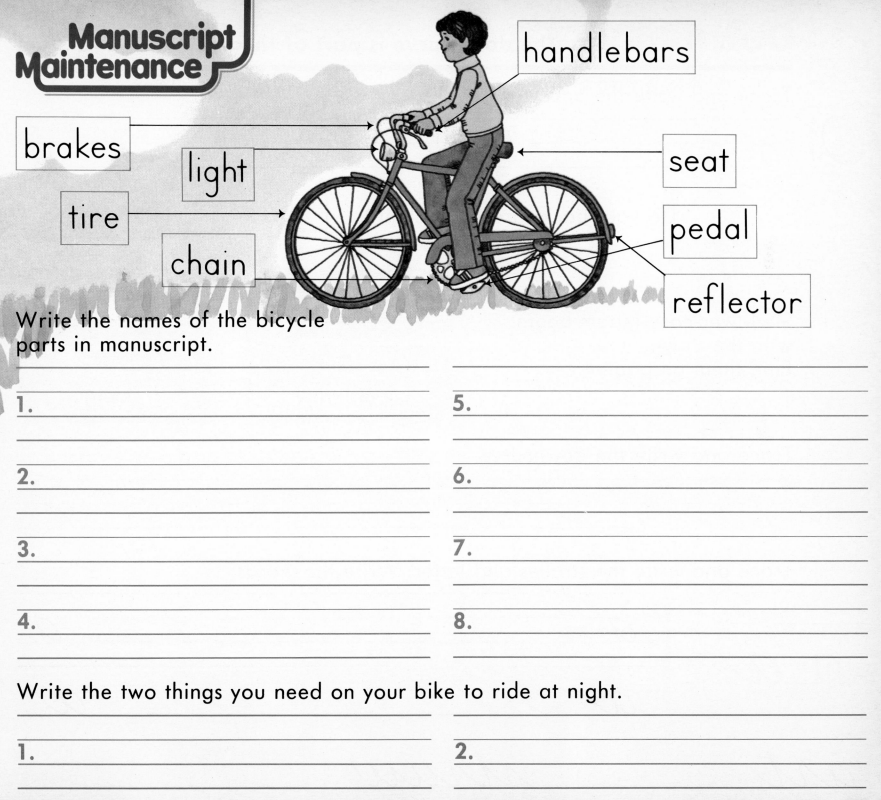

handlebars

brakes

light

tire

chain

seat

pedal

reflector

Write the names of the bicycle parts in manuscript.

1. _____

2. _____

3. _____

4. _____

5. _____

6. _____

7. _____

8. _____

Write the two things you need on your bike to ride at night.

1. _____

2. _____

Downcurve   The downcurve is part of the backward oval.

Trace and write the backward oval.

O O O — — — — — — O

Do your backward ovals slant? ☐ YES ☐ NO

Six lower-case letters begin
with the downcurve.
Find them on page 4.

CORRECT	INCORRECT
a	ω
curves wide	too straight

Trace and write the downcurve.

$\int$ $\int$ — — — — — — $\int$

Trace and write the strokes and letter. Write the words.

a a a — — — — — — a

a a a — — — — — — a

art — — $straw$ — —

28

Downcurve Letters

Trace and write the strokes and letter. Write the words.

d   d   d   _____   d

    d   d   _____   d

    d   _____   d

add _____ dad _____

ladder _____

paddle _____

Complete the sentence.

I tasted the bread.

I

Downcurve Letters

Trace and write the strokes and letters. Write the words.

g g g g   g

g   g

ga ga   ga

ge ge   ge

q q q   q

q q q   q

q   q

quite

giggle

30

Write a word to complete each sentence.

quart	guess	garage	quarter

1. The car is in the __?__ .

1. _____

2. His pencil cost a __?__ .

2. _____

3. Buy a __?__ of milk.

3. _____

4. Can you __?__ the answer?

4. _____

Match each word to the correct picture. Then write the word.

luggage •

tiger •

grapes •

quilt •

_____

_____

_____

_____

31

Downcurve Letters

Trace and write the letters. Write the words.

o   o   o   _____   _____   _____   o

oo   oo   _____   too   _____

oa   oa   _____   goat   _____

ol   ol   _____   sold   _____

c   c   c   _____   _____   _____   c

ca   ca   _____   _____   ca

cart   _____   _____   _____

co   co   _____   cocoa   _____

cl   cl   _____   cloud   _____

Working People

Do you know what jobs these people do?

Write the name of each person next to the matching number. Use the words below.

1. _____

2. _____

3. _____

4. _____

5. _____

6. _____

cook actor doctor florist grocer builder

Review Downcurve

Six lower-case letters begin with a downcurve. Write them.

_____

___ ___ ___ ___ ___ ___

Write these letter combinations in cursive.

c + *r* = _____   *c* + *t* = _____   *c* + *a* = _____

d + *o* = _____   *d* + *a* = _____   *d* + *e* = _____

Look at the manuscript words.
Write them in cursive.

g + *l* = _____

g + *u* = _____

q + *u* = _____

o + *r* = _____

o + *l* = _____

octopus _____

cactus _____

deep _____

quail _____

34

Manuscript Maintenance

Write the number words in English and Japanese.

	English		Japanese
1	one	ichi	ichi
2		ni	
3		san	
4		shi	
5		go	
6		roku	
7		shichi	
8		hachi	
9		ku	
10		ju	

Forward Oval

Trace and write the forward oval.

O O _____ O

Overcurve The overcurve is part of the forward oval motion.

Trace and write the strokes and letters. Write the words.

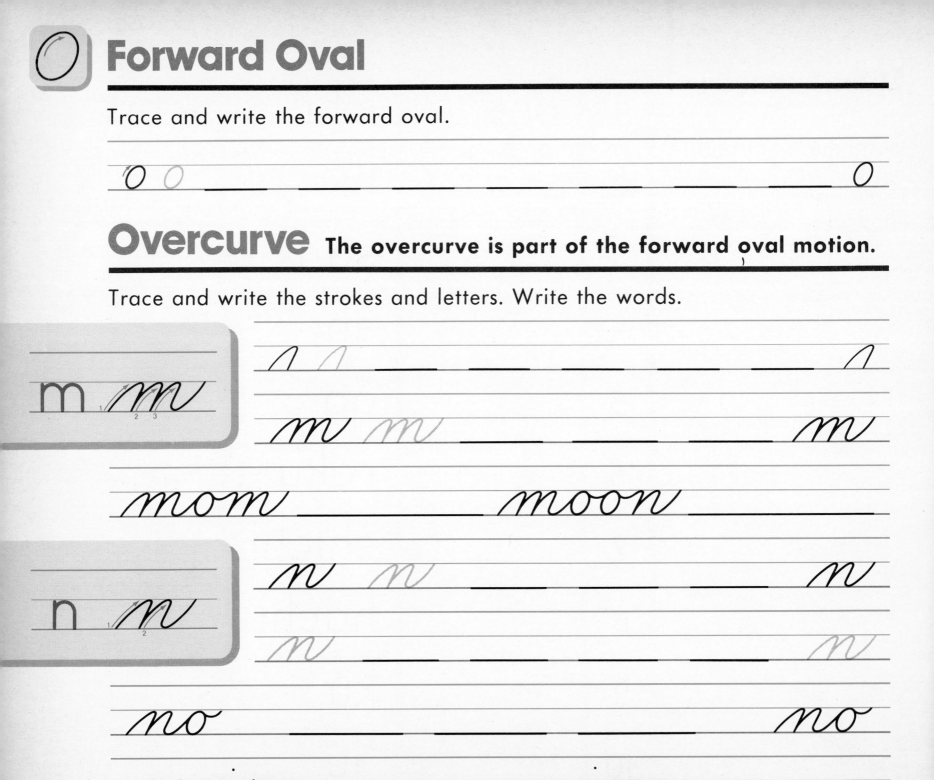

m m

n n

mom   moon

no   no

noise   nine

How Animals Use Their Feet

animals

Choose the name of an animal to answer each riddle.

I use my sharp hooves for jumping and for climbing mountains. I am a . . . . _____

My webbed feet help me paddle when I swim. I am a . . . . _____

My two front feet are like shovels with claws that I use for digging. I am a . . . . _____

Underline each **m** and **n** in the words you wrote.

mole

mountain goat

swan

Are your overcurves correct?   **YES** ☐   **NO** ☐

Overcurve Letters

Trace and write the strokes and letters. Write the words.

$\mathcal{V}$ $\mathcal{N}$ $\mathcal{N}$ $\mathcal{N}$ _____ $\mathcal{N}$

$\mathcal{v}$ $\mathcal{v}$ _____ $\mathcal{v}$

ve ve _____ $vest$ _____

$seven$ _____

X $\mathcal{x}$ $\mathcal{x}$ $\mathcal{x}$ _____ $\mathcal{x}$

x x _____ x

xe xe _____

axe _____

$taxi$ _____

Overcurve Letters

Trace and write the letters. Write the words.

y y y y y

ya ya $yard$

yes you

z z z z

zo zo zoo

$zigzag$

$pizza$

39

Six lower-case letters begin with an overcurve. Write them.

_____

_____ _____ _____ _____

Write these letter combinations in cursive.

m + i = _____   m + y = _____   y + a = _____

m + a = _____   n + g = _____   z + o = _____

n + o = _____   v + e = _____   x + e = _____

Look at the manuscript words. Write them in cursive.

yellow _____   yarn _____

fuzzy _____   monster _____

month _____   mixing _____

vine _____   oxen _____

40

Change the order of the letters to write a new word.

now _____   *lame* _____

lime _____   *net* _____

name _____   *meat* _____

vase _____   *not* _____

Change the first letter to write a new word.

fuzz _____   *box* _____

                      day _____

                      dive _____

                      came _____

                      main _____

Cursive Joinings

Write these cursive joinings.

- **undercurve to undercurve**

  le _____   *li* _____

- **undercurve to downcurve**

  fa _____   *fo* _____

- **undercurve to overcurve**

  km _____   *ky* _____

- **overcurve to undercurve**

  ye _____   *yb* _____

- **overcurve to downcurve**

  ga _____   *go* _____

- **overcurve to overcurve**

  gy _____   *gn* _____

- **checkstroke to undercurve**

  bl _____   *be* _____

- **checkstroke to downcurve**

  va _____   *vo* _____

- **checkstroke to overcurve**

  ov _____   *on* _____

Numerals

Trace and write the numerals.

1   1   1

2   2   2

3   3   3

4   4   4

5   5   5

6   6   6

7   7   7

8   8   8

9   9   9

10   10   10

Backward Oval Letters

Trace and write the strokes and letters. Write the words.

A   a   a   a   a

a   a   a   a   a

Alaska _____

C   C   C   C   C

C   C   C   C   C

Canada _____

E   E   E   E   E

E   E   E   E   E

Europe _____

Choose the correct word to begin each sentence.

Corn

Apples

Eggplants

1. _____ grows on stalks.
2. _____ grow on stems.
3. _____ grow on trees.

1. _____

2. _____

3. _____

Unscramble the sentences. Write three rules for planting.

1. *the plant Carefully seeds.*

2. *day Each garden. the weed*

3. *water plants. the Always*

Backward Oval Letters

Trace and write the letters. Write the words.

O O   O O   O

Ohio

October

D D   D D   D

David

December

Denver

Dinosaur

Owl

Dove

Ox

Donkey

Otter

Duck

Dog

Otter
Ox
Owl
Dog
Donkey
Duck
Dove
Dinosaur

Write the names of the animals in order from smallest to largest.

1. _____

2. _____

3. _____

4. _____

5. _____

6. _____

7. _____

8. _____

Trace and write the letters. Write the words.

I I

Illinois

Indiana

Idaho

J J

June

July

January

Iowa
Illinois
Indiana

James
Janet
Jason

These are names of states.
Look at the first two letters.
Are the words in alphabetical order?

YES ☐   **NO** ☐

These are names of people.
Look at the first three letters.
Are the words in alphabetical order?

YES ☐   **NO** ☐

Write each group of words in alphabetical order.

Indiana	*Irma*
Ivan	*Iowa*

1.

2.

3.

4.

Justin	*June*
Julie	*Jupiter*

1.

2.

3.

4.

49

Review

Write the letters three times each.
Put a line under your best letter.

a _____

C _____

E _____

O _____

D _____

I _____

J _____

Cloud Eater

Write these letter combinations in cursive.

An _____

Cl _____

Ea _____

Ot _____

Dr _____

In _____

Ju _____

Ad _____

Slant

Slant is determined by the position of the paper and the direction in which downstrokes are pulled. Remember to shift the paper as you write.

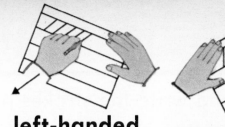

left-handed
pull toward
left elbow

right-handed
pull toward midsection

correct slant

little

incorrect slant

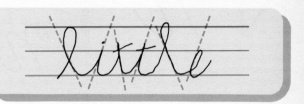

Write these words. Check your slant.

football

basket

Spacing Study the example of correct spacing.

Chris ran a race.

Write the sentence shown in the example above. Check your spacing.

	CORRECT	INCORRECT
My slant is	☐	☐
My spacing between words is	☐	☐

51

Cane Stem Letters

Trace and write the strokes and letters. Write the words.

N n

Nevada

M m

Mexico

W w

Wyoming

Some books are used for finding facts. Read the names of these books.

Write the name of the book you would use to find:

• the name of the ocean west of Africa.

_____

_____

_____

• how to weave a basket.

_____

_____

_____

• the difference between a hurricane and a tornado.

_____

_____

_____

• the names of four different trees.

_____

_____

53

Cane Stem Letters

Trace and write the letters. Write the words.

Hawaii

Kate

Xenia

Write this sentence.

Keep your teeth healthy.

You must take care of your teeth if you want them to look and stay healthy. You must eat the right foods and brush after eating. Dentists are doctors who check your teeth for decay. Hygienists clean your teeth and take X-rays. It is important to visit your dentist often.

X-rays   Hygienists   Dentists

Write a word to begin each sentence.

1. ____ check and repair teeth.
2. ____ clean teeth.
3. ____ are pictures of the teeth and roots.

1. _____

2. _____

3. _____

Unscramble the letters to write two words that tell what you must do to your teeth each day.

sbrhu

lofss

H K X

55

Cane Stem Letters

Trace and write the letters. Write the words.

U U

Uranus

Y Y

Yolanda

V V

Virginia

Putting Words in Categories

In each group of words, one word is the title of the category. Find the title and write it on the first line. Write the other three words in alphabetical order under the title.

Yellow   Colors | Ukulele   Violin

Violet   Orange | Drum   Instruments

Cane Stem Letters

Trace and write the strokes and letters. Write the words.

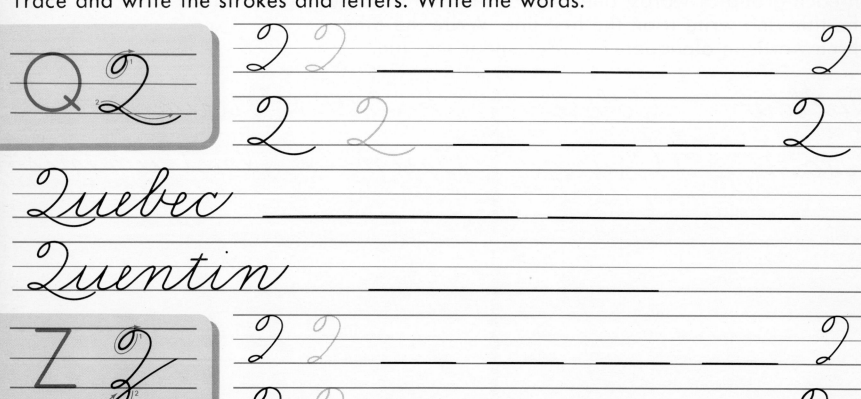

Quebec

Quentin

Zachary

Zelda

Quail

Mr. Quincy's Zoo

Kangaroo

Zebra

Walrus

Look at the picture of the zoo and find a word to answer each question.

1. Which animal in the picture has tusks?
2. Write the name of the bird in the zoo.
3. Name the animal that has a pouch.
4. Which animal has stripes?

1.

2.

3.

4.

Write the name of the zoo on this sign.

Write the eleven cane stem letters in alphabetical order.

_____

_____

_____

Write the letters in cursive. Put a line under your
best letter.

N _____   U _____

M _____   Y _____

W _____   V _____

H _____   Q _____

K _____   Z _____

X _____

Write these letter combinations in cursive.

No _____   Me _____   Wa _____

60

Unscramble the lines of the poem. Write the poem below.

As you can plainly see.

I hold out a piece of bread

Ducks are beautiful

And they take it from me!

Laura Tate, age 10

Evaluate your writing for the following elements of legibility:

	CORRECT	INCORRECT		CORRECT	INCORRECT
letter forms	☐	☐	slant	☐	☐
spacing	☐	☐	alignment	☐	☐
line quality	☐	☐	size	☐	☐

Forward Oval Letters

Trace and write the strokes and letters. Write the words.

P P

1 1 1

P P P

Penny

R R

R R R

R R

Roberto

B B

B B B

B B

Barbara

Cities

Rockville

Philadelphia

Bridgetown

Beaverton

States

Pennsylvania

Oregon

Rhode Island

Ohio

Look at the shape of each state. Use a map to find its name.
Write a sentence to tell which state each city is in.

Bridgetown is in Ohio.

Boat Stroke Letters

Trace and write the strokes and letters. Write the words.

T

Texas

F

Florida

Fact: something that is known to be true

Fiction: something that is imagined and not true

Fact or Fiction *Tortoise, Fox, Tiger*

Label each picture.

Read each sentence. If the sentence is true, write **Fact**.
If the sentence is not true, write **Fiction**.

All tortoises have four legs.

Tortoises are famous for winning races.

A fox can trick a crow into giving him cheese.

Foxes eat mice, fruit, and grass.

Tigers turn into butter when they run around trees.

A tiger is a large wild cat with yellow fur and black stripes.

65

Undercurve Letters

Trace and write the strokes and letters. Write the words.

G G

Georgia

S S

Stephen

L L

Lillian

Dog Show

Write the name of each dog next to the ribbon the dog won. Use the names below.

German Shepherd   _Greyhound_

Irish Setter   _Sheepdog_

Labrador Retriever

Review

Write the letters three times each. Put a line under your best letter.

P _____ F _____

R _____ G _____

B _____ S _____

T _____ L _____

Write these letter combinations in cursive.

Pu _____ Fa _____

Ra _____ Gl _____

Be _____ Sa _____

Th _____ Le _____

Chicken Little

Three Billy Goats Gruff

Peter Rabbit

Sleeping Beauty

Puss in Boots

Pinocchio

Write the names of the storybook characters. Put a check (✔) by the characters you know.

1. _____

2. _____

3. _____

4. _____

5. _____

6. _____

Emergency Numbers
(Dial O for Operator.)

Police   Ambulance   Doctor   Fire

Look at the words above. Write each one in manuscript next to its symbol. Use a telephone book to find these emergency numbers and write them in the blanks.

Write two more telephone numbers you use often.

Name   ### Number

Write the paragraph using words instead of pictures.

A 🐰 lives in the 🌳. It has long 🐾 and big 👀. Its strong 🐇 often carry it to safety.

_____

✓ **CHECK-UP**

My spacing between letters is ☐ INCORRECT. ☐ CORRECT.

My spacing between sentences is ☐ INCORRECT. ☐ CORRECT.

My spacing between words is ☐ INCORRECT. ☐ CORRECT.

Punctuation Marks

Punctuate the sentences below. Then write the **sentences** with the punctuation marks.

" " ! , . ?

Karen come here Matt called

What is it Karen asked

Look at this strange egg

What kind of an egg do you think Matt found?

Do your tall letters touch the headline? ☐ **YES** ☐ **NO**
Do your short letters touch the midline? ☐ **YES** ☐ **NO**
Do your tail letters fill the entire descender space? ☐ **YES** ☐ **NO**

Slant and Alignment

Write the words in each group. Write a sentence telling what you might be doing
if you were using these things. Check your slant and alignment.

bowl　　　　　　　　　　　　*measuring cup*

spoon

glue

scissors　　　　　　　　　　　*paper*

Is your slant correct?　☐ **YES**　☐ **NO**
Is your alignment correct?　☐ **YES**　☐ **NO**

Undercurve Joinings

Write these letters in cursive. Circle the undercurve ending. Write the words.

a___ c___ d___ e___ f___ h___

i___ k___ l___ m___ n___ p___

q___ r___ s___ t___ u___ x___

it

ad

in

undercurve to undercurve   *at* ___ *attic* ___

set ___ *settle* ___

undercurve to downcurve   *saddle* ___

add ___ *fact* ___

undercurve to overcurve   *fuzzy* ___

inn ___ *and* ___

Matching

undercurve to undercurve •

undercurve to downcurve •

undercurve to overcurve •

• *ra*

• *ey*

• *le*

Write at least nine words using only the letters shown below.

h i a t n u s r d e

Examples:

Circle the word that contains only undercurve-to-undercurve joinings. Draw a line under the two words that contain undercurve-to-downcurve joinings.

green little late bean

Overcurve Joinings

Write these letters in cursive. Circle the overcurve ending.

g _____ j _____ y _____ z _____

Write the words.

je	**overcurve to undercurve** jet _____ _____
	glue _____ yes _____
yo	**overcurve to downcurve** your _____
	yard _____ gas _____
gy	**overcurve to overcurve** gym _____
	hymn _____

foggy _____

Tongue Twisters

Say each tongue twister three times. Write the tongue twisters.

Jeffrey's job was to judge the juiciest jar of jam.

Gail gladly gathered the grapes growing in the garden.

Look closely at the tongue twisters you have written.
Put a line under the word in each sentence that
contains your best overcurve joining.

Checkstroke Joinings

Write these letters in cursive. Circle the checkstroke ending. Write the words.

b _____ o _____ v _____ w _____

checkstroke to undercurve

be

below _____

brave _____

checkstroke to downcurve

va

van _____

wood _____

checkstroke to overcurve

on

one _____

oxen _____

Unscramble each set of words to form a sentence. Write the sentences.

boy a The pulled wagon.

waved to I riverboat. the

blew over the wind the

balloon wall. The

 Put a line under the word in each sentence that contains your best checkstroke joining.

Gwendolyn Brooks

Gwendolyn Brooks was born in Topeka, Kansas in 1917. She often wrote about her happy childhood in her poems. Her favorite times were the holidays. She would spend hours visiting aunts, uncles, and cousins. When Gwendolyn was eleven years old she began keeping a notebook of her poetry. She has written many poems and books since that time. One of her books was called **Bronzeville Boys and Girls**.

Write the name of the poet and the name of her book.

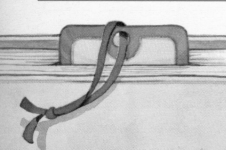

Bronzeville Boys and Girls

Keziah

I have a secret place to go
Not anyone may know.

And sometimes when the wind is rough
I cannot get there fast enough.

And sometimes when my mother
Is scolding my big brother,

My secret place, it seems to me,
Is quite the only place to be.

Gwendolyn Brooks had a secret place where she liked to go. Write the name of a secret place you would like to go to.

_____

_____

_____

Read the poem by Gwendolyn Brooks. Write the first four lines of the poem.

Cartoons

Choose the right caption for each cartoon. Write it
in the space next to the cartoon.

- *"I think we're being followed."*
- *"He is a little shy about meeting new people."*

1.

2.

CHECK-UP

	CORRECT	INCORRECT
spacing between letters	☐	☐
spacing between words	☐	☐

82

Finish the story

Write your own sentences to finish the paragraph.

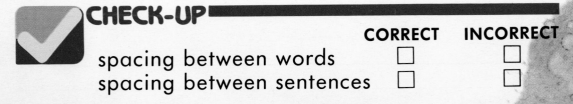

The rain stopped. I went outside. I saw huge footprints....

CHECK-UP

	CORRECT	INCORRECT
spacing between words	☐	☐
spacing between sentences	☐	☐

83

Chinese Writing

Chinese writing does not use letters of the alphabet. Chinese writing uses pictographs. Each picture means the name of a thing or an idea. Schoolchildren in China learn hundreds of pictographs.

These are Chinese pictographs.

人 *man*
田 *rice field*
木 *tree*
森 *forest*

車 *cart*
馬 *horse*
山 *mountain*
王 *king*

Write each sentence. Use words in place of the pictures.

The 人 *owned a* 田.

The 王 *lived on the* 山.

Write the story in the spaces below.
Write words in place of the pictographs.

This is the story of a 人 **who went to visit the** 王 .

He hitched his 馬 **to a** 車 **and left home.**

_____

_____

_____

_____

_____

_____

_____

_____

_____

_____

_____

_____

_____

✓ CHECK-UP

My line quality is:

too heavy ☐   too light ☐

varying ☐   satisfactory ☐

Synonyms

go - move, leave, travel

A thesaurus is a book of synonyms. Read the synonyms for the word **go**. Rewrite each sentence. Use one of the synonyms in place of the word **go**.

1. *Buses go to the city.*

_____

_____

2. *Melissa will go at noon.*

_____

_____

3. *The crowd will go slowly.*

_____

_____

 Look at the letters **o**, **a**, and **d** that you wrote.
Did you close the ovals in these letters?

YES ☐   **NO** ☐

86

Two words that mean the opposite are called **antonyms**. Write an antonym for each word below. Use the words in the list.

small

day

cold

false

go

down

tall

on

old

sad

slow

wild

night large
true short
stop new
hot off
happy up
tame fast

Write the names of these four green things.

grass _____ *peas* _____

lima bean _____

Leaves _____ _____

Read the poem. Complete the poem with the four words from above.

Green are the _____ *I eat.*

Green is the _____ *under*

my feet.

_____ *on trees are green.*

And green is a _____.

Write the name of each color by the correct crayon.
Complete each sentence with your own words.

Red Blue Purple Black Brown

Black is a lump of coal.

_____ is _____

_____ is _____

_____ is _____

_____ is _____

CHECK-UP

Are your forward oval letters correctly made?

letter **B** YES ☐ NO ☐

letter **P** YES ☐ NO ☐

letter **R** YES ☐ NO ☐

Scrambled Words

Read the story. Unscramble the underlined words and write them in the spaces below.

Once there was a _rmfare_ who bought a new _hclot_ for his _blate_. It was _der_ and _tewih_. He soon discovered that it was _gamic_. When he put it on his table he could _ishw_ for any kind of _dofo_ and it would appear.

_____   _____
_____   _____
_____   _____
_____   _____
_____   _____
_____   _____
_____   _____
_____   _____
_____   _____
_____   _____
_____   _____

	CORRECT	INCORRECT
letter formation	☐	☐
line quality	☐	☐

What food would you wish for?

_____
_____
_____
_____

90

Riddles Riddles are fun to ask and fun to answer.

Choose an answer to write for each riddle.

Q. 1. What is a volcano?

A.

Q. 2. Why can't you tell secrets in a cornfield?

A.

Q. 3. Why did the jelly roll?

A.

A. *It saw an apple turnover.*

A. *A mountain with hiccups.*

A. *Because the corn has ears.*

	CORRECT	INCORRECT
slant	☐	☐
spacing	☐	☐
alignment	☐	☐

91

Fable:
A fable is a story that teaches a lesson.
The characters in the story are often animals.

The Lion and the Mouse

Once while a lion was sleeping, a little mouse was running up and down him. When the lion awoke he grabbed the mouse and opened his jaws to swallow him. The mouse begged for his life. He promised the lion that he would do him a favor some day if he would set him free. The lion laughed and let the mouse go. Some time later, the lion was in a net set by hunters. The mouse happened to pass by. When he saw the lion, he chewed the ropes and set the lion free. The lion learned a lesson:

Little friends may prove to be great friends.

Write the lesson taught by the story.

92

Make up three questions about the story to ask a friend.
End your questions with the correct punctuation.

1
_____
_____
_____
_____

2
_____
_____
_____

3
_____
_____
_____
_____

Evaluate your sentences for the following elements of legibility:

	INCORRECT	CORRECT
letter formation	☐	☐
line quality	☐	☐
spacing	☐	☐
slant	☐	☐
alignment and proportion	☐	☐

Many years ago students wrote on small slate boards with chalk or on parchment with quill pens.

Write the sentence in cursive.

_____

_____

_____

_____

_____

_____

_____

_____

_____

_____

	CORRECT	INCORRECT		CORRECT	INCORRECT
letter formation	☐	☐	slant	☐	☐
alignment and			spacing	☐	☐
proportion	☐	☐	line quality	☐	☐

Student Record of Handwriting Skills

PAGE		NEEDS IMPROVEMENT	MASTERY OF SKILL
7	Positions paper properly.	☐	☐
7	Pulls the downstrokes in the proper direction.	☐	☐
7	Shifts the paper as writing progresses across the line.	☐	☐
9	Writes the letter **i**.	☐	☐
9	Writes the letter **t**.	☐	☐
10-11	Writes the letter **u**.	☐	☐
10-11	Writes the letter **w**.	☐	☐
10	Holds pencil properly.	☐	☐
12-13	Writes the letter **e**.	☐	☐
12-13	Writes the letter **l**.	☐	☐
14	Writes the letter **f**.	☐	☐
14	Line quality is correct.	☐	☐
16-17	Writes the letter **b**.	☐	☐
16	Alignment is correct.	☐	☐
18-19	Writes the letter **r**.	☐	☐
18-19	Writes the letter **s**.	☐	☐
22-23	Writes the letter **h**.	☐	☐
22-23	Writes the letter **k**.	☐	☐
24-25	Writes the letter **j**.	☐	☐
24-25	Writes the letter **p**.	☐	☐

PAGE		NEEDS IMPROVEMENT	MASTERY OF SKILL
28	Writes the letter **a**.	☐	☐
29	Writes the letter **d**.	☐	☐
30-31	Writes the letter **g**.	☐	☐
30-31	Writes the letter **q**.	☐	☐
32-33	Writes the letter **o**.	☐	☐
32-33	Writes the letter **c**.	☐	☐
36-37	Writes the letter **m**.	☐	☐
36-37	Writes the letter **n**.	☐	☐
38	Writes the letter **v**.	☐	☐
38	Writes the letter **x**.	☐	☐
39	Writes the letter **y**.	☐	☐
39	Writes the letter **z**.	☐	☐
43	Writes the numerals **1-10**.	☐	☐
44-45	Writes the letter **A**.	☐	☐
44-45	Writes the letter **C**.	☐	☐
44-45	Writes the letter **E**.	☐	☐
46-47	Writes the letter **O**.	☐	☐
46-47	Writes the letter **D**.	☐	☐
48-49	Writes the letter **I**.	☐	☐
48-49	Writes the letter **J**.	☐	☐
51	Slant is correct.	☐	☐

(turn page)

PAGE		NEEDS IMPROVEMENT	MASTERY OF SKILL
51	Spacing is correct.	☐	☐
52-53	Writes the letter **N**.	☐	☐
52-53	Writes the letter **M**.	☐	☐
52-53	Writes the letter **W**.	☐	☐
54-55	Writes the letter **H**.	☐	☐
54-55	Writes the letter **K**.	☐	☐
54-55	Writes the letter **X**.	☐	☐
56-57	Writes the letter **U**.	☐	☐
56-57	Writes the letter **Y**.	☐	☐
56-57	Writes the letter **V**.	☐	☐
58-59	Writes the letter **Q**.	☐	☐
58-59	Writes the letter **Z**.	☐	☐
62-63	Writes the letter **P**.	☐	☐
62-63	Writes the letter **R**.	☐	☐
62-63	Writes the letter **B**.	☐	☐
64-65	Writes the letter **T**.	☐	☐
64-65	Writes the letter **F**.	☐	☐
66-67	Writes the letter **G**.	☐	☐
66-67	Writes the letter **S**.	☐	☐
66-67	Writes the letter **L**.	☐	☐

PAGE		NEEDS IMPROVEMENT	MASTERY OF SKILL
74-75	Writes the undercurve-to-undercurve joining.	☐	☐
74-75	Writes the undercurve-to-downcurve joining.	☐	☐
74-75	Writes the undercurve-to-overcurve joining.	☐	☐
76-77	Writes the overcurve-to-undercurve joining.	☐	☐
76-77	Writes the overcurve-to-downcurve joining.	☐	☐
76-77	Writes the overcurve-to-overcurve joining.	☐	☐
78-79	Writes the checkstroke-to-undercurve joining.	☐	☐
78-79	Writes the checkstroke-to-downcurve joining.	☐	☐
78-79	Writes the checkstroke-to-overcurve joining.	☐	☐

STUDENT'S NAME